EENIE MEENIE MINIE TWEED
Eyebeam and the Real World

by Sam Hurt

Blunt Books
Distributed by AAR/Tantalus, Inc.

EENIE MEENIE MINIE TWEED

ISBN 0-9611660-2-9

Published by Blunt Books, Austin, Texas
First printing

Additional copies of this book and copies
of other books by Sam Hurt may be pur-
chased from your local bookstore or from
the distributor, AAR/Tantalus, Inc., P.O.
Box 893, Austin, TX 78767. Please en-
close an additional 50 cents for postage
and handling.

Printed and bound in the U.S.A.

Presswork and binding by McNaughton
& Gunn, Inc., Saline, Michigan.

The author wishes to thank the fol-
lowing: Clara Blain, for not getting
bored with the light board; Ray
Goldstein, for secretly writing all the
really good ones; Gordon Gidley, for
his perpetual brainstorming; Cy
Wagner, for the ski trip some 9 years
ago (I meant to drop you a card);
Jon Davis, for calling it putty; Aunt
Martha, for the knowledge that
quiche is really nothing but glorified
scrambled eggs; Kat Hager, for
oceans of little planktons that try to
chow down on your tootsies; and
Steve Patterson, for making me rich
and famous (I'll buy you a beer
sometime).

This book is respectfully dedicated to
Jun,
without whom I could hardly eat any sushi.

Introductory Prefacial Foreword

by John Schwartz

When the idea of my writing an introduction to Sam's new book comes to mind, it brings several phrases along with it. Phrases like ''puff piece'' and ''pet review.'' Phrases that suggest friendship, and a lack of objectivity. True phrases.

But if you gave this job to some guy on the street, he'd muck it up by trying to find the inner meaning to Sam's work, the Truth. That person might try to divine some political message, or perhaps a philosophical or even religious one. That person would write caca.

I may be Sam's biggest fan, but I have no illusions. The best road with *Eyebeam* is to take it on its own terms, without trying to graft some alien concept to it. Because, after all, *Eyebeam* is already about as alien as you can get. That's not to say that Sam's attitude toward Deeper Meaning is as hostile as my own. In fact, he's pretty genial about other people's interpretations of his work. In a way it reminds me of Robert Frost, who received a very long letter interpreting one of his poems. At the end of his lengthy exegesis, the correspondent wrote, ''Is this what you meant?'' Frost's return letter read, ''It is now.''

Sam would do that. That is, unless he were too busy buying new high-tech toys or playing hacky-sack. Because with Sam, distraction is not just an inconvenience—it's a life-style.

There's a character in ''Travesties,'' Tom Stoppard's play, who is trying to write biographical memoirs of Lenin, James Joyce and Tristan Tzara. It is obvious from his rambling monologue that he really doesn't know enough about any of these men to write more than a paragraph or two. Still, he is determined to write these memoirs. He keeps returning to a single phrase: "To those of us who knew him, his greatness was never in doubt."

Sometimes that's the way I feel about Sam. I have known him for several years, yet he constantly surprises me. From the days when we worked on University of Texas publications together, I have rarely felt that I know him well enough to say more than a few words about him, and doubt that even those words would be enlightening. But it's worth a try, even though he's not paying me to do this:

Sam and I have a little lunch ritual. Once a week, we drive out to a certain South Austin restaurant which is supposed to have wonderful food. It has been closed every time we have tried the place, with no indication that it would ever reopen—or, in fact, that it had ever been open. But every week Sam points his dusty brown land boat south, and we head toward disappointment and frustration again. It's partly an act of faith, and partly an affirmation of the Sisyphus in each of us. It also gets a little funnier each time.

Not everyone might think that's a fun, or funny, way to spend a part of his lunch break. Not everyone takes to *Eyebeam* right away, either. But those of you who have bought this book will understand. I think.

To those of us who know him, his greatness is never in doubt.

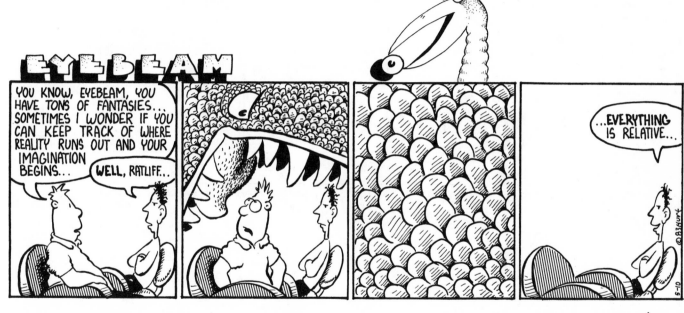

1

EYEBEAM

by Sam Hurt

Panel 1:
GOOD MORNING, EYEBEAM. YOU'RE A LITTLE LATE.

MY ALARM DIDN'T GO OFF. MY TOASTER SHORT-CIRCUITED.

6-20 ©83 Hurt

Panel 2:
...I COULDN'T FIND THE RIGHT **TIE**. MY CAR WOULDN'T START...

Panel 3:
...THE WORLD IS SPINNING THROUGH SPACE LIKE A WILD CURVE BALL. THE WHOLE **UNIVERSE** IS DRIFTING SLOWLY APART.

Panel 4:
IN SHORT, IT'S MONDAY MORNING AGAIN.

IN SHORT, YEAH.

6

EYEBEAM

by Sam Hurt

Panel 1:
VERNON- DOES IT SEEM LIKE WE'VE BEEN HAVING TO WORK EXTRA HARD LATELY?

YEAH... NOW THAT YOU MENTION IT...

Panel 2:
WHATEVER HAPPENED TO THREE-MARTINI LUNCHES AND FRIDAY AFTERNOON GOLF GAMES?

LET'S FIND OUT.

Panel 3:
YES, BOYS?

SIR, WE WERE UNDER THE IMPRESSION THAT THIS PROFESSION PROVIDED A COMFORTABLE LIVING WITH A MINIMUM OF EFFORT...

Panel 4:
WRONG! YOU HAVE TO WORK YOUR TAIL OFF TO MAKE IT BIG.

DARN!

...AND IT'S PROBABLY TOO LATE TO SWITCH.

EYEBEAM

Panel 5:
FELLAS, THE LEGAL PROFESSION DOES HAVE ITS REWARDS— WHY, SOME OF US LAWYERS ARE QUITE... UH, COMFORTABLE.

Panel 6:
... BUT IT TAKES **WORK**! -WORK AND **SWEAT**!.. -HOURS AND YEARS OF SWEAT. SWEAT AND **COFFEE**! COFFEE AND...

Panel 7:
-SAY!- THIS ISN'T THE RIGHT ATMOSPHERE AT ALL...

-I WAS THINKING THE SAME THING.

Panel 8:
...COFFEE AND **BLOOD**! THE BLOOD OF GRUESOME COURTROOM BATTLES...

HERE-**HERE**!

APPY HOUR 2-7

7

Kinda
fun
→

9

by Sam Hurt

10

EYEBEAM

by Sam Hurt

Panel 1:
THIS IS **PITIFUL!** I REALIZE THAT THIS WASN'T THE MOST INTERESTING CASE I EVER ASSIGNED...

Z. Z.

Panel 2:
...BUT IT CAN'T BE SO BAD IT PUT TWO OF MY BEST PEOPLE TO SLEEP...LET'S SEE...

Z. Z.

Panel 3:
·····YAWN·····

Z. Z.

7-7 ©83Hurt

Panel 4:
—I'M JUST GOING TO KEEP ON WORKING. THIS MUST BE SOME SORT OF WEIRD TEST...

Z. Z.

14

15

Eyebeam
LET'S SEE - WHAT SHOULD I WEAR TODAY?
WAIT A MINUTE! SOMETHING'S WRONG! THERE'S NOTHING BUT BELLBOTTOMS IN HERE!
...ASK NOT FOR WHOM THE PENDULUM SWINGS- IT SWINGS FOR YOU!
7-4 ©83 HURT
WHY, I'D RATHER DEFY FATE!...OR EVEN BE OUT OF FASHION!

EYEBEAM
by Sam Hurt
SALLY, COULD YOU HELP ME OUT WITH MY LOVE LIFE?
WHAT'S THE PROBLEM, RATLIFF?
...IT'S NONEXISTENT.
OH, YEAH.
ANYWAY, I FIGURED WITH YOUR SPECIAL EXPERTISE, YOU COULD GIVE ME SOME POINTERS...
WAIT A MINUTE. WHAT SPECIAL EXPERTISE?
...YOU'RE A GIRL...
OH, YEAH...

21

EYEBEAM

by Sam Hurt

Panel 1: AH... I LOVE BEING A LAWYER...

SHORTBREAD — AND — SNUFF ATTORNEYS AT LAW

Panel 2: ...YOU NEVER KNOW WHAT AREA OF HUMAN ENDEAVOR YOU'LL BE INVOLVED IN NEXT...

Panel 3: WHAT'S THAT? WHY, I THINK IT'S THE SOUND OF A NEW CLIENT APPROACHING!

Panel 4: I'M IN A BAD MOOD AND I WANNA **SUE**! / OUR **MOTTO**! WHAT AN OMEN!

EYEBEAM

Panel 5: SO YOU WANT TO SUE, DO YOU? / DARN TOOTIN'!

Panel 6: YOU'VE DECIDED TO CORRECT AN INJUSTICE THROUGH OUR LEGAL SYSTEM INSTEAD OF RESORTING TO BRUTE VIOLENCE. / THAT'S RIGHT.

Panel 7: IN ORDER FOR US TO BE MOST EFFECTIVE, YOU'LL NEED TO SUPPLY US WITH CERTAIN FACTS REGARDING YOUR SITUATION. / OKAY. -LIKE WHAT?

Panel 8: LIKE, WHO DO YOU WANT TO SUE? / OH...UH, I THOUGHT YOU GUYS SUPPLIED THAT.

22

EYEBEAM

by Sam Hurt

BOY... THE **PIGS** YOU MEET IN THESE BARS! - I LOVE TO THINK OF NEW WAYS TO FREAK THEM OUT...

HERE COMES ONE NOW...

HI... MIND IF I JOIN YOU?

FINE - BUT I FEEL I MUST WARN YOU - I'M A LITTLE...UH... KINKY...

THAT'S FINE. COMPLETELY STRAIGHT WOULD BE TOO - AS LONG AS YOU SHAMPOO.

NO. WHAT I MEANT WAS THAT I'M **TRISEXUAL**.

WHY, THAT'S SICK!

7-25 ©83 Hurt

EYEBEAM

♪ ...OH... ♪

♪...WHY DON'T YOU LOVE ME LIKE YOU **USED** TO DO? - HOW COME YOU TREAT ME LIKE A **WORN OUT SHOE**?♪

♪ WELL, MY EYES ARE STILL CURLY AND MY HAIR IS STILL BLUE...♪

♪ - SO WHY DON'T YOU LOVE ME LIKE YOU USED TO DO?♪

THEY'RE NOT MUCH TO **LOOK** AT, BUT THEIR MUSIC IS KINDA QUAINT.

7-26 ©83 Hurt

25

EYEBEAM

by Sam Hurt

Panel 1: BEHOLD MAN IN HIS MOST BLISSFUL STATE: DRIFTING LIGHTLY ON THE SOFT EDGE OF CONSCIOUS...

Panel 2: —SECURE IN THE PROSPECT OF CONTINUING TO DRIFT LATE INTO THE MORNING...

Panel 3: IGNORANT OF THE PRESENCE OF AN UNEXPECTED AND DISAPPROVING REPRESENTATIVE FROM THE WORLD OF RESPONSIBILITY...

MY SON, THE HUMAN ANIMAL.

7-27 ©83 HURT

EYEBEAM

Panel 4: DAD! WHAT A PLEASANT SURPRISE!

I WANTED TO GET A LOOK AT HOW YOU RUN YOUR LIFE.

Panel 5: OH... ALL RIGHT. YOU WANT SOME BREAKFAST FIRST?

NO! I WANT TO MAKE SURE YOU'RE DEVELOPING INTO A RESPONSIBLE ADULT!

Panel 6: —BUT I DID THAT ALREADY, REMEMBER?

WHEN?

Panel 7: NO, WAIT. I GUESS I WAS THINKING OF PUBERTY...

...SIGH... A WATCHED POT NEVER BECOMES FINANCIALLY INDEPENDENT.

7-28 ©83 HURT

26

29

EYEBEAM

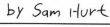

by Sam Hurt

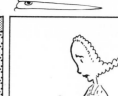

SQUISH

8-5 ©83 Hurt

EYEBEAM

SALLY, WHY ARE YOU SPRAYING THAT PAN WITH PAM?

IT KEEPS STUFF FROM STICKING...

YEAH, I KNOW. BUT WHY DID YOU SPRAY THE BOTTOM OF THE PAN?

YOU'LL SEE...

8-6 ©83 Hurt

KLANG
SQUISH

SOMETIMES IT MAKES YOU WONDER WHAT THEY DID BEFORE MODERN TECHNOLOGY...

31

Eyebeam
by Sam Hurt
OKAY, OKAY, OKAY, OKAY. -BUT I NEED TO GET READY FIRST.
THIS COULD CHANGE MY WHOLE LIFE! - SO I'D REALLY APPRECIATE IT.
HEY, RATLIFF... WHAT'S WITH SALLY? SHE LOOKS KINDA FLUSTERED.
I ASKED HER FOR SOME "IN-THE-FIELD" TRAINING ON HOW TO APPEAL TO WOMEN.
NO! SHE'S NOT GOING WITH YOU TO A SINGLES BAR!?
YUP. -SOON AS SHE GETS READY...
TRUCKIN' DOWN THE ALLEY WITH PARTY DOWN SALLY!
NO ONE MUST RECOGNIZE ME.
IF THIS WORKS, I'LL NAME MY FIRST CHILD AFTER YOU!
BUZZ OFF
HURT

33

35

EYEBEAM

by Sam Hurt

GOSH— I SURE HATE THESE DAYS WHEN I JUST CAN'T SEEM TO GET ANYTHING DONE...

—I'VE BEEN READING THE SAME LINE IN THIS MEMO OVER AND OVER FOR TWENTY MINUTES.

I'D BETTER TAKE A BREAK FOR COFFEE... AT LEAST THERE'S ONE THING COMFORTING ABOUT A DAY LIKE THIS...

...EVERYONE SEEMS TO HAVE ONE ONCE IN A WHILE...

36

37

41

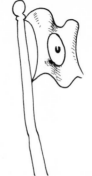

1st Peaches appearance... (she doesn't show up again for years)

eyebeam

by Sam Hurt

WELL, HI, THERE!

SALLY, THIS IS MY NIECE, "PEACHES."

GIMME CANDY.

I'M SORRY, PEACHES— I DON'T HAVE ANY CANDY.

GIMME TOYS.

I DON'T HAVE ANY TOYS, EITHER—SAY, WHAT'S WITH THIS KID?

SHE SUFFERS FROM "P.B.S."

GIMME MONEY.

8-25 ©83 Hurt

P.B.S.? WHAT'S THAT?

PRECOCIOUS BRAT SYNDROME...

GIMME CREDIT CARDS.

42

EYEBEAM

GOOBY-DOOBY DOOBY-DOO...

GOOPY DOOPY POOPY

I JUST SORT OF HAVE THIS EFFECT ON LITTLE TYKES - I THINK IT'S BECAUSE I USED TO BE ONE MYSELF...

YES, AND BECAUSE OF RATLIFF'S PARTICULAR EFFECT ON LITTLE TYKIE, WE GIVE HIM GUEST MEMBERSHIP ON THE DIAPER-DUTY ROSTER

AW, SIS!

BOY! THAT HOUSTOPOLIS IS SURE A BIG TOWN. WANT SOME CRACKER-JACKS?

THERE'S ALWAYS SOMETHING GOING ON THERE, THAT'S FOR SURE. YEAH, I'LL HAVE SOME.

ENOUGH OF THE BIG CITY, THOUGH - I'M READY FOR HOME. MAYBE SALLY WANTS SOME.

WE'VE BEEN ON THE ROAD FOR THREE HOURS. WE SHOULD BE THERE SOON. HOLD ON, I'LL ASK HER.

THREE HOURS? WE SHOULD BE HOME ALREADY!

UH-OH. MAYBE YOU WERE RIGHT ABOUT THE LOOP. HEY, NAVIGATOR - WANT SOME CRACKER JACKS?

43

45

47

EYEBAM

48

EYEBEAM

by Sam Hurt

HEY, RATLIFF! - YOU GOT A PACKAGE FROM YOUR MOTHER.

OH, **BOY**! I'LL BET IT'S ONE OF THOSE CARE PACKAGES!

ALWAYS FUN.

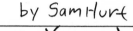

ESPECIALLY THE ONES MY MOM SENDS - SHE ALWAYS KNOWS WHAT I LIKE BEST!

BUT WHAT ARE ALL THESE LITTLE FOIL PACKAGES?

9-7 ©83 Hurt

FREEZE DRIED VIENNA SAUSAGES!

JUST LIKE GRAMMA USED TO MAKE!

49

by Sam Hurt

50

EYEBEAM

by Sam Hurt

Panel 1: BEER!

Panel 2: HERE YOU GO, DEAR— A MANLY, MOUNTAIN BREW. SURE, IT'S EXPENSIVE, BUT YOU DESERVE IT.

Panel 3: UH-OH— SOMETHING'S THE MATTER... I'VE FORGOTTEN SOMETHING.

Panel 4: FROSTED MUG! I'LL BE RIGHT BACK!

OH, IT'S SO HARD TO FIND GOOD WOMEN THESE DAYS...

Panel 5: AT THAT POINT IT WAS CLEAR THAT—

BETH!

HOLD ON, SALLY.

Panel 6: OOOPS! I LET YOU RUN OUT OF BEER— I KNOW HOW YOU HATE THAT...

DO YOU REALLY CARE? SOMETIMES I WONDER.

Panel 7: I'M SORRY, SALLY. GO AHEAD.

Panel 8: WOULDN'T IT BE EASIER TO REMAIN CONSTANTLY BY HIS SIDE TO SEE TO HIS EVERY NEED?

I'VE TRIED. IT MAKES HIM CRANKY.

BETH! OH, NEVER MIND— I'LL OPEN IT MYSELF!

51

53

54

EYEBEAM

by Sam Hurt

"YOU KNOW, EYEBEAM, YOU HAVE A SPECIAL KNACK FOR ANSWERING A QUESTION WITHOUT MAKING THE QUESTION SOUND STUPID."

"IT'S REALLY AN AMAZING TALENT. NOT MANY PEOPLE CAN DO IT."

"OKAY, OKAY— WHAT'S THE QUESTION?"

"DO YOU SAY MASSA**TU**SETTS OR MASSA**CHU**SETTS?"

"I USUALLY JUST SAY MAINE OR OREGON AND NOBODY KNOWS THE DIFFERENCE."

"—THE MAN IS UNBELIEVABLE!"

EYEBEAM

"HEY, SALLY— HOW DO YOU LIKE MY NEW SHIRT?"

"WOW, RATLIFF— THAT'S A BRIGHT SHIRT!"

"OH, I GUESS I'D CALL IT A WARM PINK AND SORT OF A POLARIZED TRAFFIC LIGHT GREEN LIKE IT?"

"WHAT? I CAN'T **HEAR** YOU!"

"HOLD ON."

CLICK

"THERE, NOW, WHAT WERE YOU SAYING?"

"YOU'D BETTER WASH THAT SHIRT SEPARATELY FOR A WHILE."

55

EYEBEAM

by Sam Hurt

Panel 1: EYEBEAM, ARE YOU AWARE THAT YOUR GIRLFRIEND, SALLY AND YOUR ROOMMATE RATLIFF HAVE BEEN... WELL, SPENDING A LOT OF TIME TOGETHER?

Panel 2: BETH, IF YOU ARE ATTEMPTING TO INTRODUCE THE INSIDIOUS FORCE OF **JEALOUSY** INTO AN OTHERWISE PURE RELATIONSHIP, FORGET IT.

Panel 3:

Panel 4: DARN!

...EXACTLY HOW MUCH TIME?

EYEBEAM

Panel 5: SALLY, DO YOU EVER GET **JEALOUS**?

ONCE IN A WHILE... I GET LITTLE **TINGES** WHEN EYEBEAM GOES TO LUNCH WITH A FEMALE ACQUAINTANCE.

Panel 6: I GET JEALOUS WHEN VICTORIA PRINCIPAL KISSES BOBBY EWING.

BOBBY EWING?

Panel 7: HE'S SUCH A DAMN FAKE!

YUP- JEALOUSY IS SURE A STRANGE PHENOMENON...

Panel 8: ...YOU NEVER KNOW WHO WILL BE HIT NEXT.

BETRAYAL!

56

57

EYEBEAM

by Sam Hurt

Panel 1:
YEAH— SOMETIMES LIFE REMINDS ME OF A SOAP OPERA, TOO.

BUT THAT'S NOT WHAT REALLY BOTHERS ME, RATLIFF.

Panel 2:
THEN WHAT DOES REALLY BOTHER YOU?

—THAT IT REMINDS ME OF A BAD SOAP OPERA THAT NOBODY WOULD BELIEVE.

AH-HA!

Panel 3:
SO!... MY GIRLFRIEND— MY SO-CALLED BEST PAL! —HAVING A COZY LITTLE CHAT! HOW DO YOU LIKE THAT!

Panel 4:
SALLY— WHAT THE HECK IS GOING ON?

TODAY'S EPISODE HAS BEEN BROUGHT TO YOU BY THE MAKER'S OF DIAL...

Panel 5:
HEY, SALLY— I'M SORRY I ACTED SO JEALOUS.

FORGET IT, EYEBEAM. I KNOW THAT JEALOUSY CAN MAKE SOMEONE IRRATIONAL.

Panel 6:
YEAH—BUT YOU AND RATLIFF!? —GIMME A BREAK! —IT'S KINDA DUMB TO CARRY IRRATIONALITY THAT FAR!

Panel 7:
HA HA HA— IMAGINE... YOU AND RATLIFF!! HAR-HA-HAR HEH-HEH...

HEH-HEH.

Panel 8:
OKAY— WHAT HAPPENED BETWEEN YOU TWO?

I CONFESS! WE HAD ONE BRIEF LITTLE EXCHANGE OF MEANINGFUL IDEAS—IT'S IN THE PAST NOW!

58

by Sam Hurt

EYEBEAM

Panel 1:
HEY, YOU GUYS— I FOUND A PIECE OF PIZZA IN YOUR FRIDGE— OKAY IF I EAT IT?
OF COURSE.
GO AHEAD.

Panel 2:
OBOY!
HOW STRANGE.
YEAH.

Panel 3:
—WAS SHE **SERIOUS**?
DO YOU THINK SHE **REALLY** HASN'T HEARD OF THE INTERNATIONAL PIZZA DOCTRINE?

Panel 4:
"LEFTOVER PIZZA, LIKE FISH IN THE STREAM OR BIRDS IN THE SKY, IS NOT SUSCEPTIBLE TO OWNERSHIP."
ENGRAVED ON THE REFRIGERATORS OF MAN THROUGHOUT HISTORY.

9-28 ©83 Hurt

59

60

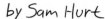

61

63

65

EYEBEAM

Panel 1: HOW DID YOUR TRIP IN THE TIME MACHINE GO, EYEBEAM?

NOT SO HOT. THERE WERE COMPLICATIONS, AND NOTHING GOT... ACCOMPLISHED.

Panel 2: TOO BAD, HEY, WHERE'S SALLY BEEN?

SHE'S NOT GOING TO BE AROUND FOR A WHILE — DUE TO ONE OF THE COMPLICATIONS.

Panel 3: OH, WHY DO I **DO** IT, RATLIFF? TIME IS THE THREAD THAT TIES REALITY TOGETHER— WHY DO I USE DANGEROUS TECHNOLOGY TO TANGLE IT UP IN KNOTS?

Panel 4: IT'S PROBABLY JUST YOUR WAY OF TRYING TO GET ATTENTION.

RATLIFF, CHILD PSYCHOLOGY ISN'T GOING TO HELP ME RIGHT NOW. — AND IT COULD **HURT** YOU.

EYEBEAM

Panel 5: RATLIFF! HEY, LONG TIME, NO SEE!

NORMAN! —HEY, IT SEEMS LIKE I JUST HEARD SOMETHING ABOUT YOU THE OTHER DAY...

Panel 6: YEAH? WHAT WAS IT?

OH, **YEAH!**

...UH... ...WELL... UH... I HEARD YOU WERE A- ...UH...

Panel 7: —YOU MUST HAVE HEARD ABOUT MY DECISION TO ABANDON THE OLD CLOSET.

WHAT'S THIS? —YOU HAD A CARD PRINTED UP?

Panel 8: I FIGURED, HEY— WHY NOT MAKE IT OFFICIAL?

"NORMAN FAYE —Total Gay"

67

EYEBEAM

by Sam Hurt

MMMMMMMMMMM

MMMMM.....

-GREEEEEEEEOMP
-BLOOP
-dolio...
-dolio...
-dolio..

...SOMETIMES I WONDER IF OUR LIVES ARE BEING CONTROLLED BY MYSTERIOUS, UNKNOWN FORCES...

YOU KNOW, RATLIFF, A PERSON'S MIND IS SORT OF LIKE AN ICEBERG...

WHAT DO YOU MEAN?

WELL, THERE'S THE TINY LITTLE TIP THAT EVERYONE KNOWS THROUGH THE THINGS YOU SAY AND DO...

...AND BENEATH THE SURFACE IS THE HUGE, UNSEEN MASS THAT EVEN YOU YOURSELF CAN NEVER KNOW—THINK ABOUT IT SOMETIME.

OKAY...

HMM...I THINK HE MAY HAVE A POINT...

68

69

EYEBEAM

by Sam Hurt

...SO IN CONCLUSION, THE AMBIGUITY IN THE CONTRACT SHOULD BE CONSTRUED IN FAVOR OF OUR CLIENT, SINCE THE OTHER GUY WROTE IT... OKAY, **SHIFT**!

NOW, IN THIS OTHER CASE, A GUY USED A CHAINSAW TO CUT DOWN THE ATTENDANCE AT HIS AEROBIC DANCE CLASS. WE REPRESENT THE MAKERS OF THE LEOTARDS... -THE **LEOTARDS**?

RRRRRING

UH-OH... SHIFT!

YEAH...I READ THAT FILE. -I'M AFRAID THE OTHER SIDE IS GOING TO ARGUE THAT OUR CLIENT GAVE IMPLIED CONSENT TO EVERYTHING THAT HAPPENED TO HIM BY ATTENDING THAT IGUANA SEX RALLY...OK..BYE.

NOW, SHIFT BACK.

10-13 ©83 Hurt

...LUCKY FOR ME MY BRAIN HAS A GOOD TRANSMISSION.

SALLY'S BEEN GONE FOR A GOOD WHILE NOW - DO YOU MISS HER?

MISS HER? HMMMM... I HADN'T REALLY THOUGHT ABOUT IT...

...I MEAN, IT WAS HER DECISION TO LEAVE - SHE THOUGHT I WAS BEING POSSESSIVE... **HA**!

...SHE PROBABLY THINKS I MISS HER, BUT... NAW...I DON'T.

WELL, I SURE MISS HER..

LOOK- IF **ANYBODY** IS GONNA MISS HER, IT'S GONNA BE ME!

10-14 ©83 Hurt

70

EYEBEAM

by Sam Hurt

Panel 1:

FEELS GOOD TO GET OUT ON THE OLD HIGHWAY ONCE IN A WHILE.

YEAH — AND ESCAPE THAT CLOSED-IN FEELING OF THE CITY.

Panel 2:

YOU GET A NEW PERSPECTIVE ON THINGS OUT HERE.

— A SENSE OF WHO YOU ARE — AND WHAT LIFE IS ALL ABOUT.

Panel 3:

BUT THERE'S SOMETHING EVEN **MORE** IMPORTANT THAT WE CAN GET OUT OF THIS!

OH, YES! — THAT WHICH SUPERSEDES ALL ELSE...

Panel 4:

...GOOD BARBEQUE!

GAS

FRED'S SHACK

RIBS

OPEN

HOMEMADE PIES

SCREEEEEE...

©83 HURT 10-15 THANKS McCRIMINAL

71

EYEBEAM

by Sam Hurt

BLUGH – WHAT A WAY TO START OUT A MONDAY – TAKING OUT THE FUZZBALL TRASH!

.. KINDA CLEARS OUT THE OLD SINUSES, THOUGH...

EXCUSE ME, SIR – I'M WITH CHANNEL X! – ACTION WITNESS NEWS.

WHAT CAN I DO FOR YOU?

OUR HELICOPTER REPORTED A BIG PILE OF TRASH IN THIS NEIGHBORHOOD

I STILL SAY IT'S RATLIFF'S TURN TO TAKE IT OUT!

72

10-17 ©83 Hurt

EYEBEAM

by Sam Hurt

OKAY, MR. SLUDGE - I'VE BEEN ASKED TO HELP PREPARE YOU FOR THE TRIAL.

WHAT'S TO PREPARE? - LET'S GO SUE THEIR BUTTS!

WELL, AS THE PLAINTIFF, IT'S VERY IMPORTANT THAT YOU MAKE A GOOD IMPRESSION ON THE JURY.

-SO WE CAN MILK 'EM FOR EVERY PENNY, RIGHT?

UH, WE HAVE EXPERIENCE WITH THE SUBTLE TOUCH THAT'S SOMETIMES REQUIRED.

EXACTLY WHAT ARE YOU TRYING TO TELL ME?

GET ANOTHER SUIT AND KEEP YOUR MOUTH SHUT.

...AHEM... YOUR HONOR...

...DISTINGUISHED MEMBERS OF THE JURY.....

-WHAT MY CLIENT SEEKS FROM YOU TODAY IS SOMETHING VERY SIMPLE- ...HE SEEKS JUSTICE...

PSST.... HEY!

ONE MOMENT...

MONEY! I'M SEEKING MONEY!

LET ME HANDLE THIS, OKAY?

73

EYEBEAM

by Sam Hurt

AT LAST! - A MACHINE TO REVERSE THE POLARITY OF PHYSICAL JUXTAPOSITIONS!

- OF COURSE, THOSE OF DIM PERCEPTION WILL FAIL TO SEE ITS VALUE, OR EVEN ITS EFFECTIVENESS- -THEIR LOSS.....

I STAND ON THE THRESHOLD OF A NEW AGE.... OKAY, HERE GOES!

10-20 ©83 Hurt

WELL... COME ON.... DO SOMETHING...

74

HEY, EYEBEAM- WHAT ARE YOU WORKING ON NOW?

IT'S A DOOHICKEY I JUST INVENTED, BUT I HAVEN'T FIGURED OUT WHAT IT DOES YET.

WELL, HECK! -LET'S JUST TURN IT ON AND FIND OUT!

-THAT'S THE PROBLEM- IT'S BEEN ON FOR TWO HOURS AND NOTHING'S HAPPENED!

WELL, I WOULDN'T BE TOO SURE ABOUT THAT!

WHAT DO YOU MEAN, RATLIFF?

10-21 ©83 Hurt

MY TOENAILS JUST GREW! RIGHT INTO THE FLOOR!

NOW, THIS COULD BE DEVELOPED INTO SOMETHING WITH COMMERCIAL POTENTIAL!

75

EYEBEAM

by Sam Hurt

EYEBEAM - I'M GETTING WORRIED ABOUT SALLY! -I HAVEN'T SEEN HER IN WEEKS!

YEAH! -I'M WORRIED, TOO...

OKAY... EXPLAIN ONCE MORE... WHERE'D SHE GO?

SHE HIJACKED MY TIME MACHINE...SHE WANTED TO VISIT HUMPHREY BOGART.

-SEEMS LIKE SHE'D BE **BACK** BY NOW...

HEY - WHAT THE HECK ARE YOU GUYS TALKING ABOUT?

NOTHING! IT'S JUST A SEPARATE PLOT LINE THAT DOESN'T CONCERN YOU!

THERE WERE A HELL OF A LOT OF THINGS THEY DIDN'T TELL ME WHEN I HIRED ON TO THIS OUTFIT!

10-24 ©83 HURT

LORDY, LORDY, **LORDY**! WHAT A MANURE-INSPIRING DAY!

MY JOB IS IN PERIL... MY LIFE IS IN A RUT... AND MY CAR IS IN THE SHOP...

NOTHING COULD SAVE A DAY LIKE THIS- UNLESS MAYBE...

...A PRETTY GIRL SHOWED UP IN A TIME MACHINE

NEED A LIFT?

10-25 ©83 HURT

76

EYEBEAM

by Sam Hurt

WELL, HI THERE, SALLY...

HELLO, EYEBEAM.

NICE TO SEE YOU.

YEAH— IT'S BEEN A WHILE.

WERE'NT WE HAVING SOME SORT OF MISUNDERSTANDING WHEN WE LAST SPOKE?

PROBABLY.

-CAN I ASSUME FROM OUR BEHAVIOR THAT WE'VE RESOLVED OUR DIFFERENCES?

YOU CAN DO WHATEVER YOU WANT— I'M GONNA SMOOCH...

10-26 ©83 HURT

77

EYEBEAM

Panel 1: OKAY, SALLY, LEVEL WITH ME.... WHAT HAPPENED BETWEEN YOU AND BOGART WHEN YOU BORROWED MY TIME MACHINE?

Panel 2: EYEBEAM, WHO WAS IT WHO SAID RELATIONSHIPS THAT HAPPENED BEFORE WE MET SHOULD BE LEFT IN THE PAST?

UH... ME.

WELL, THIS WAS BEFORE WE WERE BORN...

Panel 3:

Panel 4: ...AND I'M THE ONE WHO SPENT ALL THAT TIME AND MONEY ON LAW SCHOOL!

10-27 ©83 HUK

Panel 5: YOU KNOW, BETH I GOT SO DISGUSTED WITH EYEBEAM'S BACKWARDS, POSSESSIVE BEHAVIOR THAT I TOOK HIS TIME MACHINE INTO THE PAST...

Panel 6: ...BUT IT TURNS OUT, MEN USED TO BE EVEN LESS ENLIGHTENED THAN THEY ARE NOW...

Panel 7: THAT'S TOO BAD...

OH, WELL— IT HELPED TEACH ME TO BE SATISFIED WITH WHAT I'VE GOT...

Panel 8: HEY! I WONDER ABOUT MEN IN THE FUTURE!

I CHECKED— THEY ALL WEAR MOHAWKS.

10-28 ©83 HUK

78

79

EYEBEAM

by Sam Hurt

Panel 1:
ROD— SHARE AN INNERMOST FEELING WITH ME.

WOULD A DEEP-ROOTED ANXIETY DO?

80

Panel 2:
WHY, SURE.

OKAY— YOU KNOW HOW I ALWAYS SEEM PRETTY CONFIDENT ABOUT MY MASCULINITY?

Panel 3:
—YOU REALIZE YOU'RE THE STUDLIEST FELLOW IN RECORDED HISTORY.

WELL, WAY DOWN DEEP, I DON'T FEEL COMPLETELY WHOLE ABOUT MY MANHOOD.

© 83 HURT 10-31

Panel 4:
BUT WHY ON EARTH NOT?

YOU SEE, I'VE NEVER HAD JOCK-ITCH.

EYEBEAM

by Sam Hurt

HI, EYEBEAM. I'M TAKING YOUR PET LEECHES FOR A WALK.

THAT'S NICE OF YOU, RATLIFF — HAVING A GOOD TIME?

YES SIRREE! THEY'RE A LITTLE SLOW BUT IT GIVES ME A CHANCE TO TAKE IN THE SCENERY.

THAT'S SWELL.

CUTE LITTLE RASCALS — YOU NEVER HEAR A PEEP OUT OF THEM.

UH-OH!

NO! BAD BOYS! NO!

82

©83 Hurt 11-3

EYEBEAM

by Sam Hurt

BOY! -THIS WEATHER HAS REALLY BEEN SOMETHING! -SO UNPREDICTABLE!

...IN A WAY, I GUESS LIFE IS LIKE THAT...

I MEAN, YOU NEVER KNOW EXACTLY HOW TO PREPARE FOR IT...

THAT'S ME! -I WANT A RICH, MEANINGFUL EXISTENCE, BUT I'M NOT SURE WHAT TO WEAR...

-BUT ARE YOU SURE THEY'RE SAFE?

TAKE IT FROM ME, THEY'RE GONNA LOOK REALLY BOSS ON YOU.

HERE- PUT IT ON MY CARD...

YES, SIR.

THANK YOU, COME AGAIN.

...WHOEVER INVENTED HIGH-HEEL JOGGING SHOES OUGHTA BE SHOT!

83

YOU KNOW, LIFE IS REALLY BEAUTIFUL—I FEEL LIKE I'M IN TOTAL HARMONY WITH NATURE...

OF COURSE, IT'S NOT ALL A BED OF ROSE PETALS—YOU GOTTA STAY ON YOUR TOES, IN CASE LIFE THROWS BUMPS OR WADS OF CHEWING-GUM INTO YOUR PATH.

RING

HELLO? OH, HI, DAD... YEAH, I'VE BEEN LOOKING FOR A JOB—IT'LL TAKE ANOTHER FEW MONTHS. OR MORE... A WEEK!? AW, DAD!

...LIFE REALLY SUCKS!

HEY, EYEBEAM—MY DAD TOLD ME TO GET A JOB—WHAT DO YOU THINK I'D BE GOOD AT?

HEY!—I'M NOT PUTTING YOU ON THE SPOT, AM I?

OH, GOODNESS NO! —JUST GIVE ME A MINUTE...

84

EYEBEAM

IT'S NOT GOING TOO WELL, IS IT, RATLIFF?

HELP WANTED

WELL, THE JOB MARKET ISN'T THE BEST IT'S EVER BEEN, BUT DON'T GET DISCOURAGED.

HELP WANTED

ASLO, SINCE YOU'VE NEVER HAD A JOB BEFORE, YOU PROBABLY DON'T REALIZE THAT IT JUST TAKES A LITTLE PERSISTENCE, THAT'S ALL.

PAT PAT

HELP WANTED

©83 Hurt 11-9

LOOKS LIKE THE ASTRONAUT POSITIONS HAVE ALL BEEN FILLED.

HEY! HERE'S ONE: "HUMAN PAPERWEIGHT NEEDED — NO EXPERIENCE NECESSARY."

HELP WANTED

85

EYEBEAM
by Sam Hurt

YOU KNOW, ROD—I'VE BEEN THINKING...

NOW, YOU KNOW PRETTY GIRLS SHOULDN'T GET MIXED UP IN THAT SORT OF THING...

NO—SERIOUSLY! I'M TRYING TO FIGURE OUT WHAT KEEPS US TOGETHER.

IT'S SIMPLE—I LIKE YOU BECAUSE YOU TREAT ME BETTER THAN A MERE MORTAL.

...AND YOU LIKE ME BECAUSE I ACTIVATE EVERY HORMONE IN YOUR LUSCIOUS LITTLE BODY...

...YOU'RE SO CUTE WHEN YOU USE BIG WORDS!

NOW, THAT'S MORE LIKE IT.

11-12
©83 HURT

EYEBEAM! HEY, **EYEBEAM**! IT HAPPENED! —I GOT A **JOB**!

SLAM

I DID LIKE YOU SAID—I KEPT CONTINUING TO PERSEVERE— AND IT WORKED!

GREAT! WHAT KIND OF JOB DID YOU GET?

UH... WELL...

UH-OH—IT'S NOT SOMETHING THAT GOES AGAINST YOUR PRINCIPLES, IS IT?

11-10
©83 HURT

I'M GONNA BE THE GUY AT THE T.V. STATION WHO TURNS UP THE VOLUME WHEN THE COMMERCIALS COME ON

WHAT'S IT PAY? WILL YOU BE ABLE TO AFFORD A BODYGUARD?

86

EYEBEAM
by Sam Hurt

HELLO, DAD? I JUST WANTED TO LET YOU KNOW I GOT A JOB! — I WORK AT THE T.V. STATION, I TURN UP THE SOUND WHEN THE COMMERCIALS COME ON.

EXCELLENT! A "TELEVISION BROADCAST VOLUME ENGINEER"... AN IMPORTANT LINK IN THE FREE ENTERPRISE CHAIN!

WOW! FOR THE FIRST TIME, I FEEL LIKE I'M **WORTH** SOMETHING IN MY FATHER'S EYES!

HELLO, JONES? McNUBB HERE — BUY STOCK IN ALL COMPANIES THAT MAKE THOSE T.V. REMOTE CONTROLS WITH MUTE BUTTONS...

87

EYEBEAM

by Sam Hurt

©83 Hurt

11-16

89

EYEBEAM

by Sam Hurt

90

EYEBEAM

by Sam Hurt

©'83 Hurt 11-19 Thanks (But NoThanks) to Richard H.

91

by Sam Hurt

93

94

95

96

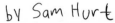

97

by Sam Hurt

I REMEMBER WHEN I WAS A YOUNG LAW STUDENT...

...THINGS WERE SO **SIMPLE** THEN. THE LAW HELD SUCH **PROMISE**!

...NOW I FIND THAT RIGHT AND WRONG PLAY HIDE AND SEEK AMID THE LAW'S VAST SWAMP OF GREY AREAS AND LOOPHOLES...

LIGHTEN UP, POPS- YOU'RE GETTING THE **RENT** PAID, AREN'T YOU?

TRUE.

98

VERNON- LET ME TELL YOU A FEW THINGS ABOUT LIFE...

OH, NO!

-IT'S A LONG ROW TO HOE- YOU GOTTA PAY THE PIPER AND YOU GOTTA PAY YOUR DUES- AND SOMETIMES YOU GOTTA ROB PETER TO PAY PAUL.

.....WOW!...

-DO YOU REALIZE I JUST SAVED YOU ABOUT 20 YEARS OF HARD- EARNED EXPERIENCE?

YEAH- THE LEAST I CAN DO IS PICK UP THE CHECK.

101

103

104

105

107

109

110

111

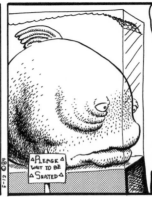

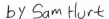

by Sam Hurt

SOMEHOW, ANOTHER DAY HAS PASSED AND I HAVEN'T DONE A THING. A WHOLE SEMESTER'S WORTH OF READING TO DO.

...ONLY IF I SPEND EVERY WAKING MOMENT STUDYING MY TAIL OFF WILL I HAVE EVEN A FAINT GLIMMER OF HOPE...

-THERE'S ONLY ONE THING FOR A GUY LIKE ME TO DO AT A TIME LIKE THIS...

...LEARN TO PLAY HACKY-SACK!

...IT WAS ONLY A MATTER OF TIME.

PIT

PAT

PA-TUNK

"COME WATCH ME PLAY HACKY-SACK," HE SAYS, "I'M REALLY GETTING GOOD"..."BUT RATLIFF," I SAY "I'M DRINKING A BLOODY MARY."..."DON'T WORRY," HE SAYS.

114

by Sam Hurt

115

117

119

by Sam Hurt

WHAT CAN I DO FOR YOU TODAY, EYEBEAM?

WELL, SIR, I'M GOING TO HAVE TO ASK FOR SOME TIME OFF...

YOU'D BETTER HAVE A GOOD REASON!

I GUESS I SHOULD HAVE MENTIONED THIS ON MY RESUMÉ, BUT, YOU SEE, I'M A COMIC STRIP CHARACTER...

...AND, WELL, THE BOOK I'M CURRENTLY IN IS ABOUT TO DRAW TO A CLOSE... SO I WON'T BE AROUND FOR A WHILE...

AFTER THIS, I'LL THINK TWICE ABOUT HIRING ANY COMIC STRIP CHARACTERS.

YOU'RE GONNA HAVE TO WATCH OUT FOR THE DEPARTMENT OF LABOR...

12-14 ©83 HURT

WELL, ROD - IF THE AUTHOR'S GOING TO TAKE A BREAK, MAYBE YOU COULD DRAW THE STRIP...

HEY, YEAH!... OF COURSE, I'D HAVE TO CHANGE THAT STUPID NAME...

IT SHOULD BE NAMED AFTER YOU, ANYWAY.

"STUDMUFFINS" - BY J. RODNEY RUTHERFORD, III

..OR "SNUGGLEBUNS" - BY ROD AND BETH RUTHERFORD.

ROD AND BETH RUTHERFORD!?

SURE... COMIC STRIP CHARACTERS GET MARRIED TOO, YOU KNOW.

...NOT IN MY STRIP, THEY WON'T!

12-15 ©83 HURT

120

121